Book F

Specific Skill Series

Following Directions

Richard A. Boning

Fifth Edition

D1304067

SRA/McGraw-Hill

Columbus, Ohio

Cover, Back Cover, ZEFA/Germany/The Stock Market

SRA/McGraw-Hill

*A Division of The **McGraw·Hill** Companies*

Send all inquiries to:
    SRA/McGraw-Hill
    8787 Orion Place
    Columbus, OH 43240-4027

ISBN 0-02-687936-0

 7 8 9 IPC 02 01 00

To the Teacher

PURPOSE:
FOLLOWING DIRECTIONS is designed to develop skill in reading, understanding, and following instructions and directions. Proficiency in this basic skill is essential for success in every school subject and in nonacademic activities as well.

FOR WHOM:
The skill of FOLLOWING DIRECTIONS is developed through a series of books spanning ten levels (Picture, Preparatory, A, B, C, D, E, F, G, H). The Picture Level is for pupils who have not acquired a basic sight vocabulary. The Preparatory Level is for pupils who have a basic sight vocabulary but are not yet ready for the first-grade-level book. Books A through H are appropriate for pupils who can read on levels one through eight, respectively. **The use of the *Specific Skill Series Placement Test* is recommended to determine the appropriate level.**

THE NEW EDITION:
The fifth edition of the *Specific Skill Series* maintains the quality and focus that has distinguished this program for more than 25 years. A key element central to the program's success has been the unique nature of the reading selections. Nonfiction pieces about current topics have been designed to stimulate the interest of students, motivating them to use the comprehension strategies they have learned to further their reading. To keep this important aspect of the program intact, a percentage of the reading selections have been replaced in order to ensure the continued relevance of the subject material.

In addition, a significant percentage of the artwork in the program has been replaced to give the books a contemporary look. The cover photographs are designed to appeal to readers of all ages.

SESSIONS:
Short practice sessions are the most effective. It is desirable to have a practice session every day or every other day, using a few units each session.

SCORING:
Pupils should record their answers on the reproducible worksheets. The worksheets make scoring easier and provide uniform records of the pupils' work. Using worksheets also avoids consuming the exercise books.

To the Teacher

It is important for pupils to know how well they are doing. For this reason, units should be scored as soon as they have been completed. Then a discussion can be held in which pupils justify their choices. (The Integrated Language Activities, many of which are open-ended, do not lend themselves to an objective score; thus there are no answer keys for these pages.)

GENERAL INFORMATION ON *FOLLOWING DIRECTIONS*:

FOLLOWING DIRECTIONS focuses attention on four types of directions. The *testing and drilling* directions are like those in most textbooks and workbooks. Mastery of this type, so vital to school success, is stressed throughout FOLLOWING DIRECTIONS. The second type of direction is found in science books and involves *experimenting*. Such material requires the reader to find an answer to a problem or provides the reader with an example of practical application of a principle.

The third type of direction, *assembling*, deals with parts or ingredients and the order and way in which they are put together. Here the purpose is to make or create, rather than to solve a problem or demonstrate a principle.

Directions which tell how to do something are *performing* directions. They accent the steps in learning to do something new. The focus is on the performance rather than on the product.

SUGGESTED STEPS:

On levels A-H, pupils read the information above the first line. Then they answer the questions *below* this line. (Pupils are *not* to respond in writing to information *above* the first line; they are only to study it. Pupils should not write or mark anything in this book.) On the Picture Level, pupils tell if a picture correctly follows the directions. On the Preparatory Level, pupils tell which picture out of two correctly follows the directions.

Additional information on using FOLLOWING DIRECTIONS with pupils will be found in the **Specific Skill Series Teacher's Manual**.

RELATED MATERIALS:

Specific Skill Series Placement Tests, which enable the teacher to place pupils at their appropriate levels in each skill, are available for the Elementary (Pre-1–6) and Midway (4–8) grade levels.

About This Book

Following directions is like trying to find your way in a strange place by using a road map. If you follow the directions correctly, you will get where you want to go. If you do not understand the directions, or if you make mistakes in following them, you will become lost.

Reading directions is different from reading a story or an article. When you read directions, you should read slowly and carefully. You should reread anything you do not understand and find out the meanings of any special terms that are used. When you are following directions, you need to follow them in the right order. Direction words, such as *top*, *bottom*, *right*, and *left*, are especially important.

In this book, you will read four different kinds of directions. You will read directions that are like the directions you often find on tests and in workbooks. You will read directions that tell you how to conduct experiments and directions for putting things together. You will also read directions for doing things, such as playing a game.

After you read each set of directions, you will answer questions about the directions. One question is about the purpose of the directions. Others are about details in the directions. Read each set of directions carefully so that you can answer the questions about them.

DIRECTIONS: An obstacle course is easy to design and set up. Here are a few suggestions of things to use as obstacles: a ladder, a large cardboard box, and a hoop. From these you will get ideas for using other things you happen to have around. You will need some space outdoors, in a yard or field. First put the ladder flat on the ground. Try to step between the rungs one foot at a time. Start over if you step outside, miss a space, or put both feet in the same space. Secondly, open both ends of the cardboard box to make a tunnel. Crawl through it. Thirdly, place the hoop on the ground. Pick it up and spin it around your waist ten times. You can continue to make your obstacle course more difficult by adding more obstacles.

1. These instructions give ideas for constructing—
   (A) an observation deck   (B) a golf course
   (C) a ladder   (D) an obstacle course

2. The ladder is placed—
   (A) on the ground   (B) against a building
   (C) over a stream   (D) in the garbage

3. A tunnel can be made from a cardboard box by—
   (A) cutting off the top   (B) removing all the tape
   (C) opening both ends   (D) sinking it into the ground

4. Your course can be made more difficult by adding other—
   (A) advantages   (B) cylinders
   (C) triangles   (D) obstacles

DIRECTIONS: The proper care and handling of books will make them last longer. Books should be kept at an even temperature, from 68 to 74 degrees Fahrenheit (F), with 40 to 60 percent relative humidity, or water in the air. If it's too dry, paper becomes brittle, and if it's too damp, mold can grow on it. When handling books, don't pull them off the shelf by the top of the spine. Don't put paper clips, newspaper clippings, or flowers in books. Don't turn down corners or use objects, such as pencils, to mark your place. If books get wet, freezing them stops further damage until they can be properly restored by an expert.

1. These instructions give ideas for preserving—
   (A) **books**
   (B) **newspapers**
   (C) **flowers**
   (D) **structures**

2. An ideal temperature is—
   (A) **40 to 60 degrees F**
   (B) **68 to 84 degrees F**
   (C) **50 to 60 degrees F**
   (D) **68 to 74 degrees F**

3. Too much moisture causes the growth of—
   (A) **mold**
   (B) **roots**
   (C) **leaves**
   (D) **skin**

4. Wet books can often be restored if they are first—
   (A) **dried**
   (B) **opened**
   (C) **identified**
   (D) **frozen**

DIRECTIONS: What a bicycle rider wears is important. A good helmet will protect the head from a hard fall. The right shirt—one made of polypropylene—will draw moisture off the body and keep the rider cool. Shorts should have fairly long, close-fitting legs. Regular cycling shoes make pedaling more efficient and prevent feet from cramping. Many bicycle riders wear padded gloves for comfort and safety. The padding helps absorb the shock of turns and bumps and saves the hands from getting scraped if the rider falls.

1. This article tells you—

    (A) how to ride a bicycle

    (B) how to repair a bicycle

    (C) how to put a bicycle together

    (D) what to wear when bicycle riding

2. The proper covering for the head is a—

    (A) straw hat

    (B) helmet

    (C) scarf

    (D) baseball cap

3. A shirt made of polypropylene will—

    (A) billow out

    (B) draw off moisture

    (C) prevent colds

    (D) fit loosely

4. To absorb the shock of the road, wear—

    (A) a seat belt

    (B) padded gloves

    (C) a padded shirt

    (D) glasses

DIRECTIONS: First look in the newspapers for a cartoon, sketch, or comic strip you would like to transfer onto a piece of white paper. Next mix up a batch of the following ingredients: one tablespoon of white soap powder, one-half pint of boiling water, and two tablespoons of turpentine. Wear rubber gloves to protect your hands from the turpentine. Stir the mixture together until it is cool. Then dampen the face of your chosen newspaper cartoon with a coating of this solution. Use a wad of cotton for a sponge. While the newspaper is still wet, put the cartoon face down on a sheet of drawing paper. Rub the newspaper with the bottom of a spoon. After the print has been transferred to the paper, wait for it to dry, and then trace the outline with black ink.

---

1. These instructions tell you how to—
   - **(A) transfer newspaper cartoons**
   - **(B) start your own comic strip**
   - **(C) color the cartoons**
   - **(D) use tracing paper**

2. The solution should contain boiling water, turpentine, and—
   - **(A) cotton wads**
   - **(B) baking soda**
   - **(C) black ink**
   - **(D) white soap powder**

3. Put the cartoon face down on the drawing paper—
   - **(A) while the cartoon is wet**
   - **(B) before wetting the cartoon**
   - **(C) after the cartoon dries**
   - **(D) after you transfer the print**

4. After the transferred cartoon has dried,—
   - **(A) wet it with the solution**
   - **(B) rub it with a spoon**
   - **(C) trace the outline with ink**
   - **(D) rub it with soap powder**

DIRECTIONS: The only ingredients you will need are a cup of water and one and three quarters of a cup of granulated sugar. First boil the water. Then take it off the heat and stir in the sugar. For colored rock candy, add a drop or two of food coloring. Then let the solution cool. Next carefully heat a glass jar by running hot water over it, and pour in the sugar solution. Let the solution stand while you tie a string around a pencil that is longer than the mouth of the jar. Make sure that the length of the string is the same as the height of the jar. Then place the pencil across the top of the jar with the string hanging down into the solution. As the solution stands for several days, the sugar crystals will form around the string.

1. These directions show you how to—
   (A) **make rock candy**
   (B) **make a sugar syrup**
   (C) **freeze sugar**
   (D) **purify sugar**

2. Before stirring the sugar into the water,—
   (A) **tie the string to the pencil**
   (B) **boil the water**
   (C) **heat a glass jar well**
   (D) **put the string into the water**

3. After the sugar solution cools,—
   (A) **pour it into a cool jar**
   (B) **pour it into a heated jar**
   (C) **stand a pencil in it**
   (D) **add food coloring**

4. The sugar crystals will form—
   (A) **around the pencil**
   (B) **in a few days**
   (C) **almost immediately**
   (D) **when you add more sugar**

DIRECTIONS: First find a small, shallow cardboard box (a shoebox lid will do the job as well). Be sure to lay out a few newspapers around the spot where you are planning to work. Next mix two cups of soap flakes and three-quarters of a cup of water in a bowl. Stir until you have a smooth paste. Then put a layer of soap paste in the bottom of the cardboard box. Make sure that you have at least one-quarter inch of paste in the box. Then build your map on the soap base. Use more paste to make buildings or mountains, and cut into the paste base to form rivers. Make smooth surfaces by rubbing the base with wet fingers. After the three-dimensional map has dried overnight, paint it with tempera paint.

1. This article shows you how to—
   - (A) make a sandcastle
   - (B) soap up a shallow box
   - (C) make soap statues
   - (D) make a three-dimensional map

2. Make the paste with three-quarters cup of water and—
   - (A) three-quarters cup of soap flakes
   - (B) one cup of soap flakes
   - (C) one-quarter cup of soap flakes
   - (D) two cups of soap flakes

3. Start to build the map on the soap base when the base is—
   - (A) one-quarter inch deep
   - (B) painted
   - (C) dry
   - (D) one inch deep

4. Paint the map—
   - (A) before it has dried
   - (B) before forming rivers
   - (C) with soap flakes and water
   - (D) after it stands overnight

DIRECTIONS: First remove all rocks and wood pieces from the tent site. Then spread a plastic sheet or rain poncho out on the ground. In order to keep the tent clean, unwrap the tent itself on the tarp. Next separate all the stakes, lines, and poles. Be sure to keep track of all the ropes and stakes. Face the tent opening away from the campfire site, and keep the tent itself about twenty feet from the fire. Drive the stakes and tie the guy lines. Next raise the tent at the pole, and hammer additional stakes. Smooth out the floor. Make sure all stakes and lines are secure. When the tent is up, make sure that the opening is closed to keep out insects and that the ventilation flaps are open to let in fresh air.

1. These directions show you how to—
    (A) put up a tent
    (B) tie the guy lines
    (C) build a lean-to
    (D) start a campfire

2. Before spreading the plastic on the ground,—
    (A) smooth the floor
    (B) close the tent door
    (C) remove rocks from the area
    (D) separate the stakes and lines

3. After driving the stakes and tying the guy lines,—
    (A) raise the tent at the pole
    (B) close the tent door
    (C) unwrap the tent
    (D) spread out the tarp

4. When the tent is up,—
    (A) drive the stakes
    (B) keep the opening propped open
    (C) open the fresh-air flaps
    (D) separate the stakes

DIRECTIONS: Before you use a thermometer, shake it down. Grasp the end opposite the bulb between the thumb and first finger. Snap it down vigorously. You should keep doing this until the temperature reading is below 98.6°. Be careful that the thermometer doesn't slip from your fingers. Insert the bulb end of the thermometer under your tongue. Make sure your mouth is kept closed. No talking! Keep it there for three minutes. Remove the thermometer by the end opposite the bulb. Hold it horizontally with the sharp edge facing you. Roll it until the column of mercury, a liquid metal that is used to measure temperature, comes into view. The degrees are marked off and numbered. The normal temperature is marked with an arrow or in red. If your temperature is around 98°, everything is fine. If it gets much above this, call a doctor.

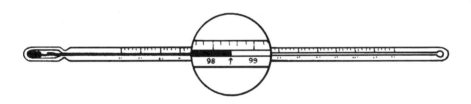

1. The purpose of these directions is to teach you how to—
    (A) keep your mouth closed   **(B) clean a thermometer**
    (C) find the mercury column   **(D) use a thermometer**

2. The first thing you must do is—
    (A) shake it down   **(B) open your mouth**
    (C) look for the mercury   **(D) call a doctor**

3. Your temperature should be around—
    (A) 98°   **(B) 90°**
    (C) 103°   **(D) 88°**

4. Remember to—
    (A) keep your mouth open   **(B) keep talking**
    (C) keep your mouth closed   **(D) put the tongue under the thermometer**

DIRECTIONS: All the materials you need can be found in your home. First get a small juice can, a wire coat hanger, a drinking glass, and some sand or regular table salt. Next punch a hole in the bottom of the juice can. Then shape the coat hanger into a stand that will support the can. Place the can on the stand, bottom down, and put the glass underneath. Now fill the can with sand or salt. Record the length of time it takes for all the sand to empty from the can to the glass. The size of the hole determines the rate at which the sand runs out of the can. Use this homemade timer when playing games or when cooking.

1. These instructions will help you build a—
   - (A) sandglass timer
   - (B) juice can
   - (C) drinking glass
   - (D) salt shaker

2. The next step after you punch a hole in the can is to—
   - (A) measure the size of the hole
   - (B) record the time
   - (C) pour the sand
   - (D) make the coat hanger into a stand

3. The glass is used for—
   - (A) weighing the sand
   - (B) holding up the can
   - (C) pouring the sand into the can
   - (D) catching the sand from the can

4. The size of the hole in the can determines—
   - (A) what time it is
   - (B) how big the glass should be
   - (C) how fast the sand runs out
   - (D) how much sand to use

DIRECTIONS: The TV weather report announces a tornado warning! It tells you to take shelter. Turn off all electrical devices. If you have a battery-powered radio, keep it with you. If you live in a mobile home, go to a community storm shelter. In a house or apartment, do not open windows. Open windows do not prevent severe wind damage. Go to a basement and get under a table or workbench. If you have no basement, go to an inner area far from windows, such as a hallway, inner bedroom, or closet. Crouch under a mattress or other thick bedding. Stay sheltered until the storm is over.

1. This paragraph was written to tell you how to—
   - **(A) take shelter during a storm**
   - **(B) turn off the electricity**
   - **(C) draw a plan of your home**
   - **(D) choose a battery radio**

2. Opening windows is not helpful because—
   - **(A) you will get cold**
   - **(B) rain will soak the floor**
   - **(C) it wastes time**
   - **(D) wind damage still occurs**

3. Getting under a workbench or table protects you from—
   - **(A) rain**
   - **(B) lightning**
   - **(C) cold**
   - **(D) flying or falling material**

4. Halls, inner bedrooms, or closets are safest because—
   - **(A) they are stronger**
   - **(B) they are away from the wind**
   - **(C) they have a workbench**
   - **(D) they have been painted recently**

DIRECTIONS: Your dog should be directly in front of you. Tie a long rope to its collar. Then let it play for a while. Say, "Come." Then pull the animal all the way to you. Pet it gently. Repeat this same procedure of pulling and petting again and again. After this, do not use the voice signal. Instead, just give a short pull on the rope. The dog will come to you to be petted. If not, continue to pull on the rope. Repeat this several times. Each time, use the rope less and less. Finally, untie the dog and ask it to come to you. If the animal walks away, follow it very slowly. Otherwise, it will think you are starting a chase. Make the dog come back to the starting place and begin training again with the rope.

1. From this article you will learn how to—
   - **(A) get your dog to come to you**
   - **(B) groom your dog**
   - **(C) walk your dog**
   - **(D) use voice commands**

2. After pulling your dog to you,—
   - **(A) follow the dog**
   - **(B) feed the dog**
   - **(C) pet the dog**
   - **(D) let the dog return to the starting place**

3. If the dog does not come to you to be petted,—
   - **(A) let the dog play a while**
   - **(B) continue to pull**
   - **(C) ignore the dog**
   - **(D) untie the dog**

4. If the dog walks away,—
   - **(A) call the dog back**
   - **(B) follow very slowly**
   - **(C) shout at the dog**
   - **(D) tie the dog up**

DIRECTIONS: Assume a slightly crouched position. Make sure that both feet are touching the rubber. You should hold the ball with your palm up. The first two fingers and the thumb should grip the seams. Move the ball back in an underhand backswing. Your eyes should be directly on your target. As the backswing begins, move your opposite leg forward. This places the weight of the body on the side of the throwing arm. The forward swing of the arm begins, and the weight is transferred from the back to the front foot. You must complete the forward stride to coincide with the release of the ball. Be sure to follow through with the arm motion—smoothly and gracefully.

1. This article was written to show you how to—
    (A) **make a double play**   (B) **pitch a softball**
    (C) **return a softball to the pitcher** (D) **throw a runner out at first**

2. Your eyes should be directly on the—
    (A) **runner**   (B) **first base**
    (C) **target**   (D) **pitcher**

3. As you begin the backswing, move your—
    (A) **opposite hand**   (B) **opposite leg**
    (C) **opposite shoulder**   (D) **head to the right**

4. It is important to remember to—
    (A) **grip the ball with four fingers**   (B) **transfer your weight**
    (C) **keep your head away from the bat** (D) **hold the ball palm down**

A. Exercising Your Skill

There are different kinds of directions. Some directions are the kind you see in workbooks and on tests. Some directions tell you how to do or make something. Others tell you how to carry out an experiment.

Read these sets of directions. Think about what the directions tell you to do. Match each set of directions with a title from the box. Write the numbers 1, 2, 3, and 4 on your paper. Next to each number, write the title that fits the directions.

Experiment Directions	Game Directions
How-To Directions	Workbook Directions

1. Read about ducks. Decide how the kinds of ducks are the same or different. Then underline the answer to each question.

2. You can make bongo drums with two coffee cans—one large and one small—their lids, and some masking tape. Snap the lids onto the cans. Turn the cans upside down and stand them on a table. Have someone hold the cans while you wind tape around them to hold them together. Turn the cans right side up, and drum away with your hands.

3. Which reflects the sun's rays better, black or white? Put two thermometers in the sun. Cover one with a white cloth and one with a black cloth. After half an hour, take off the cloth and check the temperature. Which thermometer shows a lower temperature?

4. You will need seven or eight people and several different objects. All the players sit in a circle and sing a song together. Pass the objects around. When the song is over, everyone who is caught with an object has to make up a skit about it. When the skits are finished, start again. Skits can't be repeated. If someone can't think of a new skit, he or she is out!

B. Expanding Your Skill

Discuss the different kinds of directions with your classmates. Answer the following questions.

- How are all directions the same? How are they different?
- What kinds of directions list materials?
- What kinds of directions usually have illustrations?

C. Exploring Language

The following things can help make directions clear.

- a title
- a list of materials at the beginning
- steps listed in the order to be followed
- steps that are numbered or use time-order words
- illustrations

Choose one of the sets of directions in Part A. On your paper, rewrite the directions to make them clearer. If materials are used, list them first. Number the steps or use time-order words to show the order to follow. If you think any more information should be given, add it. Add illustrations if you think they will help. Give the directions a title.

D. Expressing Yourself

Choose one of these activities.

1. Help a young child, such as a second-grader in your school, learn how to do something. Give clear, step-by-step directions. Demonstrate how to do it yourself, if that would help. Be patient. If the child doesn't understand your directions, try explaining it another way.

2. Make up a game. Write directions for how to play the game. Make sure that the directions are clear, and that they include all the steps that the players need to know. Then play the game with your classmates.

3. Write out a set of simple directions for doing something. Include at least five steps. Write each step on a separate piece of paper or index card. Do not number the steps. Mix up the papers or cards. Challenge your classmates to put the steps in order. Give them a time limit. See who can put the steps in order the fastest.

DIRECTIONS: For proper cleaning, jewelers recommend using hot soapy water and a small brush. Use ammonia to loosen dirt on all jewels but pearls. Scrub each part of the jewelry with the bristles of the brush so that the entire setting will be cleaned. Rinse in hot water and dry with a soft cloth or tissue paper. Rub gold jewelry with some chamois, a kind of soft leather, but apply very little pressure on gold-plated articles. Wash silver with soap and hot water, and polish it with a good silver polish. Stone-bead necklaces should be restrung once a year. Costume jewelry should be cleaned in mildly warm water to avoid damage. Clean tarnished jewelry with dry baking soda on a brush. Never use hot water or ammonia on plastics; sponge them with warm, soapy water.

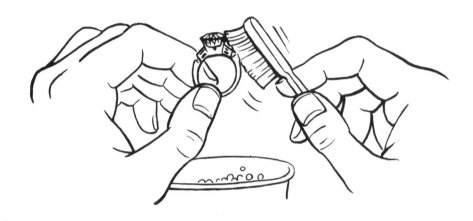

1. These instructions show you how to—
   (A) care for jewelry
   (B) buy and sell jewelry
   (C) make costume jewelry
   (D) know the value of jewelry

2. Use ammonia on all dirty jewels but—
   (A) gold
   (B) stone beads
   (C) silver
   (D) pearls

3. Before polishing silver,—
   (A) rub it with soft chamois
   (B) wash it with hot water and soap
   (C) clean it in warm water
   (D) wash it with baking soda

4. To clean plastic jewelry, use—
   (A) hot water
   (B) ammonia
   (C) mildly warm water
   (D) soft chamois

DIRECTIONS: Avoid keeping food in the freezer for a long stretch of time. Date your food packages as you place them in the freezer. Store your commercially frozen foods in their original packages. If you plan to keep fresh meat in the freezer longer than two weeks, wrap the original package in special freezer material. Put new food packages on the coldest surface of the freezer so they will freeze quickly. Put your packages in the freezer so that their labels can be easily read. Save time by doubling the recipe when preparing foods at home; bake two pies and freeze one of them. If at all possible, do not refreeze thawed, uncooked food.

1. This article teaches you how to—
   - **(A) use a refrigerator properly**
   - **(B) store food in the freezer**
   - **(C) prepare foods at home**
   - **(D) buy frozen foods**

2. You should wrap fresh meat in special freezer material if—
   - **(A) it's wider than one foot**
   - **(B) it will be frozen over two weeks**
   - **(C) it was expensive**
   - **(D) it is more than two pounds**

3. Put new food on—
   - **(A) the back of the freezer**
   - **(B) the coldest spot of the freezer**
   - **(C) special wrappers**
   - **(D) the refrigerator**

4. A bad policy is to—
   - **(A) double the recipe of home-prepared foods**
   - **(B) refreeze uncooked food**
   - **(C) date your freezer foods**
   - **(D) freeze new food quickly**

UNIT 15

DIRECTIONS: Check with the Bureau of Mining in your state, or any state you plan to visit on vacation. There is gold to be found in a surprising number of states. You can buy a gold pan at a sporting goods store. Dip the pan into the bottom of the stream so that it is more than half full of dirt and gravel. Hold the pan in the water. As you do, remove larger pieces of dirt, clay, and larger rocks by letting the stream carry them away. Move the pan in a circle. Every few seconds bring the motion to a halt. This will allow any heavy flakes of gold to sink to the bottom. Other particles will wash away. When nothing is left in the pan but gold and heavy sand, pick out the gold flakes and start all over again.

1. The purpose of this article is to tell you how to—
   - **(A) buy a gold pan**
   - **(B) wade in a stream**
   - **(C) do hard-rock mining**
   - **(D) pan for gold**

2. Get rid of pieces of clay and larger pieces of rock by—
   - **(A) letting the stream carry them away**
   - **(B) straining them through a cloth**
   - **(C) giving them away**
   - **(D) crushing them**

3. Gold settles to the bottom of the pan because—
   - **(A) it is easily caught**
   - **(B) it floats well**
   - **(C) of its weight**
   - **(D) it is attracted to sand**

4. After you have nothing left in the pan but sand and gold,—
   - **(A) pick out the flakes of gold**
   - **(B) open a bank account**
   - **(C) start over**
   - **(D) throw a party**

DIRECTIONS: To begin with, be sure to lubricate, or oil, all movable parts and bearings. Next, let the air out of the tires. Always check the tire spokes. Tighten them if loose; replace them if broken. Then wipe the spokes and all chrome parts with a rag soaked in oil. Attend to the seat next. Rub it with saddle soap. Work the soap in as deeply as you can; this treatment will preserve the leather. Then store the bicycle by hanging it from the ceiling of your cellar or attic. Make hooks from half-inch iron rods attached to eye-hooks. Screw them into the ceiling. If you can't hang the bicycle, at least turn it upside down. Keep in mind that the winter storage room should be cool.

1. These instructions show you how to—
   (A) build a bicycle
   (B) paint a bicycle
   (C) ride a bicycle
   (D) store a bicycle

2. Before letting the air out of the tires,—
   (A) lubricate all moving parts
   (B) hang the bicycle upside down
   (C) wipe the chrome
   (D) rub the seat with soap

3. The spokes should be wiped with—
   (A) a clean rag
   (B) an oil-soaked rag
   (C) saddle soap
   (D) warm water

4. The bicycle should be stored—
   (A) in a warm room
   (B) with air in its tires
   (C) hanging or upside down
   (D) resting on its wheels

DIRECTIONS: First collect the following equipment: thin wire, a pair of snippers, florist's thread, and some floratape for binding stems and wires. The thread and floratape should be available at local flower shops. Next test different flowers for their ability to last. Reject any flowers that will not remain fresh for at least three days. Gather your flowers early in the morning. Then place them in cold water for several hours to make them harden. After this, tape each flower and place it in a cool place until you are ready to assemble it into a corsage. To hold the flowers in place and to allow them to be bent in different directions, wire each flower. Small flowers must be wired to a central stem.

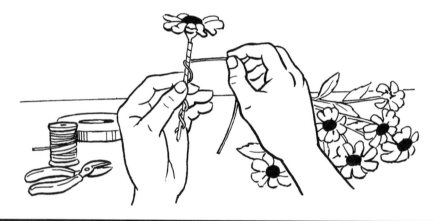

1. This article tells you how to—
   (A) grow beautiful flowers
   (B) use a pair of snippers
   (C) sell flowers
   (D) make a corsage

2. After collecting the materials, you next—
   (A) wire the flowers together
   (B) place the flowers in warm water
   (C) test the flowers for lasting power
   (D) gather the flowers at night

3. To harden the flowers,—
   (A) wire them to a central stem
   (B) tape them together
   (C) place them in cold water
   (D) cut them in the morning

4. Smaller flowers must be—
   (A) wired to a main stem
   (B) rejected
   (C) placed in a hot place
   (D) put in the middle of the corsage

UNIT 18

DIRECTIONS: Bring your body to the surface by kicking vigorously. Place both hands on the gunwale, or upper edge of the canoe's side. Choose a point where it is narrow enough to reach across. Keep your hands about shoulder's-width apart. Your arms should be straight but not stiff. Reach across the canoe with your right hand. Put as much weight as you can on the other side of the canoe so that it won't flip over. Keep the right elbow high. Kick your legs. Lift and pull with your arms. Slide your upper body across the boat. Now do a quarter turn and sit down in the canoe. Your legs will be the last part of you to come aboard.

1. The directions show you how to—
   (A) do a swan dive   (B) empty a canoe
   (C) board a canoe from the water (D) rescue a friend

2. Press on the far side so that the canoe—
   (A) won't flip over   (B) will sink
   (C) won't escape   (D) won't drift away

3. Be sure to—
   (A) keep your arms bent   (B) get in feet first
   (C) keep the right elbow high   (D) choose the widest point

4. After you have your upper body across the canoe,—
   (A) go to sleep   (B) turn your body and sit down
   (C) grasp the gunwale   (D) yell for help

DIRECTIONS: Before you start, you'll need a pet shampoo, two thick towels, a washcloth, some cotton, white vinegar, a comb, and a hair dryer. A divided sink is the best spot to wash your cat. Fill both sides with warm water. Next find your cat and trim its nails (to prevent painful scratches). Immerse the cat quickly in the water, and soap it completely. Work from the cat's head to the tail, talking gently all the while. Wash the face with a washcloth and the ears with a damp cotton ball. Now dunk your cat in the rinsing water. Add a little vinegar to the rinse water to prevent tangles. After rubbing the cat down with a towel, blow dry its fur with a hair dryer.

1. These instructions teach you how to—
   - (A) **enter your cat in a show**
   - (B) **feed your cat**
   - (C) **trim a cat's nails**
   - (D) **give your cat a bath**

2. Before trimming the cat's nails,—
   - (A) **fill the sink with hot water**
   - (B) **fill two sinks with warm water**
   - (C) **soap the cat thoroughly**
   - (D) **blow its fur dry**

3. To clean the cat's ears, use—
   - (A) **a towel**
   - (B) **a brush**
   - (C) **vinegar**
   - (D) **a damp cotton ball**

4. Add a little vinegar to the—
   - (A) **soapy water**
   - (B) **pet shampoo**
   - (C) **pet's food**
   - (D) **rinse water**

DIRECTIONS: First prepare the area where you'll be working. Wear a plastic apron. Melt your wax in a double boiler over a low heat; never use a direct flame. Keep the temperature of the melting wax at about 175°-200°F. If the wax should catch fire, place a lid over it or smother it with baking soda. Never throw water into hot wax. Handle this part of the project with extreme care. To add color to your wax, throw in some ordinary wax crayons. Remember that the color will lighten when the wax hardens. Next find a suitable mold. A milk carton, gelatin mold, or any plastic container will do. Before pouring the wax into the mold, allow it to cool slightly. Pour the wax slowly and as close to the mold as possible. Before the wax hardens, add a wick.

1. These directions tell you how to—
   (A) make a wax candle
   (B) make a wax statue
   (C) make a candle mold
   (D) wax your furniture

2. After preparing the work area,—
   (A) melt wax over an open flame
   (B) melt wax in a double boiler
   (C) melt some crayons
   (D) make a wick

3. To smother a wax fire,—
   (A) use water
   (B) use a double boiler
   (C) throw in crayons
   (D) put on the lid

4. Before pouring the wax into the mold,—
   (A) let the color lighten
   (B) heat the mold
   (C) heat the wax to 250° F
   (D) let the wax cool slightly

DIRECTIONS: First make sure that the celery is washed well to remove any dirt which may cling to the branches. Celery hearts may be served as they are, after first making them crisp by placing them in ice water. You can also make celery curls very easily. Just slit the pieces of celery into lengthwise slices and drop them into ice water. After several hours, the slices will curl back. Cooked celery also makes a fine side dish. Just slice and cook the stalks in boiling salted water for ten minutes. The cooked celery may be served with butter or a delicious cheese sauce. Another taste sensation is celery braised, or slowly cooked, in a small amount of bouillon, a flavorful broth.

1. These directions show you how to—
   (A) slice celery
   (B) boil salted water
   (C) remove celery hearts
   (D) prepare celery in different ways

2. Before preparing celery, you must always—
   (A) wash the celery thoroughly
   (B) remove the celery hearts
   (C) place it in ice water
   (D) braise it in bouillon

3. Celery hearts may be served after—
   (A) boiling them in salted water
   (B) slicing them
   (C) crisping them in ice water
   (D) cooking them

4. When cooking celery, you must leave it in boiling water for—
   (A) 30 minutes
   (B) 15 minutes
   (C) one hour
   (D) 10 minutes

DIRECTIONS: For this experiment you will need a live frog. Find one in a nearby pond or purchase a specimen from a local pet shop. Then collect a one-quart wide-mouthed jar, enough mud to fill the jar about two inches deep, a cake pan, some water, a few ice cubes, and a thermometer. After putting the mud in the jar, fill the container with water to within an inch of the top. Put the frog into the jar. Place the jar in the cake pan and take the temperature of the water. As you place ice cubes around the jar, continue to take the temperature of the water. After several minutes, the frog will submerge, or go underwater, and stop moving. This experiment shows how frogs put themselves into a deep sleep during winter months. It will not hurt the frog.

1. This experiment shows—
   - **(A) why frogs like jars**
   - **(B) how frogs sleep through winter**
   - **(C) how to record water temperature**
   - **(D) how to build a frog home**

2. Before filling the jar with water, you should—
   - **(A) put mud in the jar**
   - **(B) put the frog in the jar**
   - **(C) take the jar's temperature**
   - **(D) surround the jar with ice**

3. While placing ice around the jar, you should—
   - **(A) continue taking the water temperature**
   - **(B) fill the jar with mud**
   - **(C) put the frog in the jar**
   - **(D) put the jar in the cake pan**

4. The frog will stop moving—
   - **(A) after you add the ice**
   - **(B) before you add the mud**
   - **(C) before you add the ice**
   - **(D) after you take it from the jar**

DIRECTIONS: To clean your home more carefully and efficiently, write instructions for cleaning each room on a 3x5 card. Pick up before you vacuum. Carry everything you need for cleaning in a pail or plastic bag. Be sure to include a soft paintbrush to dust carvings, lampshades, and pieces of china; lighter fluid to remove scuff and crayon marks; and a brown, felt-tipped permanent marker to cover up scratches on dark furniture. To speed things up, use two buckets and two mops or sponges: one for washing and one for rinsing. When washing a wall, start at the bottom, as dripping from above can cause "clean streaks" that are hard to remove.

1. This article gives you ideas for more efficient—
   (A) cleaning of your car
   (B) use of water
   (C) heating of your home
   (D) cleaning of your home

2. On a 3x5 card, write instructions for—
   (A) measuring curtains
   (B) cleaning each room
   (C) washing the walls
   (D) mopping the floors

3. For removing scuff and crayon marks, use—
   (A) lighter fluid
   (B) a plastic bag
   (C) an eraser
   (D) a paintbrush

4. When washing a wall,—
   (A) use a felt-tipped pen
   (B) start at the top
   (C) start at the bottom
   (D) use a paintbrush

DIRECTIONS: Writing a letter is a way to meet and talk to another person on paper. All your writing supplies—envelopes, paper, stamps, address book, pens—should be kept in one place, so that you'll have them handy whenever you're in the mood to write. You might prefer to use a typewriter or word processor instead of a pen. Before you begin, try to picture your friend. Think of the last time you talked together, either in person or on paper. What news about you would he or she be interested in? Take a deep breath and start to write as if you were about to talk. The more you write, the easier it will be to put down what you want to say.

1. This article was written to help you—
   (A) learn word processing
   (B) use a typewriter
   (C) buy writing supplies
   (D) write letters

2. All writing supplies should be—
   (A) 8" x 11"
   (B) decorated paper
   (C) in one place
   (D) under lock and key

3. Before you begin, decide what your friend would like to—
   (A) earn
   (B) know
   (C) say
   (D) drive

4. Make your writing sound like you are—
   (A) eating
   (B) climbing
   (C) talking
   (D) flying

A. Exercising Your Skill

Directions give you steps to follow. The steps should be followed in order. The steps may be numbered, or they may use words like *first*, *next*, *then*, and *finally*. Read the following directions.

PIGPEN CODE

First draw a tic-tac-toe grid and a large X. Then draw another one of each. Next put a dot in each space in the second set. After that, put one letter in each space.

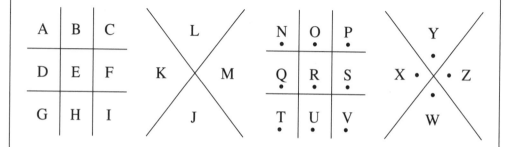

To spell a word in code, first look at where the letter comes in a grid or in an X. Then draw the lines that appear around that letter. If there are dots in the space, draw them too. Now look at these letters.

B. Expanding Your Skill

Write the codes for the other twenty-two letters of the alphabet. Compare your codes with your classmates'. Be very careful to copy the codes exactly. If you put a dot in the wrong place, your code could send the wrong message!

C. Exploring Language

The directions below are out of order, and they do not use any time-order words. Rewrite the directions so that the steps are in the right order. Then add time-order words to help show the order of the steps to be followed.

KEY WORD SHIFT CODE

Above the real alphabet, write your key word followed by all the other letters of the alphabet, leaving out the letters in the key word.

Choose a key word. It should be as long as possible, but it should not repeat any letters.

Write the alphabet across the page, all on one line. This is your real alphabet.

Be sure to tell your friend the key word you are using.

Every real letter should have a code letter above it.

To put a message into code, substitute the code letter for the real letter.

D. Expressing Yourself

Choose one of these activities.

1. Use one of the codes on these pages to write your own secret message. Then exchange messages with a classmate, and try to figure out each other's messages.

2. Find a book of codes (also called *ciphers*) in the library. Share the directions for using a code with a classmate. Send messages to each other in code.

3. Make up a code or cipher of your own. Write a set of directions for using the code. Be sure to include examples to make the directions clear. Then explain the directions to a classmate so that you can exchange secret messages.

4. Go to the library and find out how Morse Code works. Practice giving a simple message in Morse Code. Work with some of your classmates. Try to "read" each other's Morse Code messages.

DIRECTIONS: To plant roses in the fall, first pick out the planting location. Next dig a hole fifteen inches wide and eighteen inches deep. Add a quart of peat moss with a half cup of fertilizer. Mix this well. Then position the rosebush on a mound in the center. Spread out the roots naturally. Scatter more soil over the roots and firm the ground with your foot. Fill the rest of the hole with water and let it drain. Fill with more soil and pat it firmly in place. The plant is now ready for the soil mound which will protect it from freezing and thawing. Mound this soil around and over the rosebush to a height of about one foot. After growth begins in the spring, remove the mound.

1. These directions show you how to—
   - **(A) trim roses**
   - **(C) grow bigger roses**
   - **(B) plant roses in the summer**
   - **(D) plant roses in the autumn**

2. After digging the hole,—
   - **(A) avoid adding water**
   - **(C) put the bush on the bottom**
   - **(B) add peat moss and fertilizer**
   - **(D) wrap up the rose's roots**

3. After arranging the roots naturally,—
   - **(A) position the bush on a mound**
   - **(C) scatter soil over the roots**
   - **(B) dig the hole**
   - **(D) add the fertilizer**

4. The protective mound should reach a height of—
   - **(A) fifteen inches**
   - **(C) eighteen inches**
   - **(B) two feet**
   - **(D) one foot**

DIRECTIONS: You should be directly behind the boat. The driver should keep a straight course, at a constant speed of twenty miles an hour. Make sure that you alternately lift one ski just about a foot high parallel to the water and then the other. Take the toe of your ski out of the water first, and then the back part of the ski. Otherwise the toe will catch in the water and you may lose the ski or your balance. If you wobble when you have one ski raised above the water, move your ankle to keep the ski level and in a straight line. As you begin to get used to it, raise your foot higher and higher until you can bring your knee up to your waist.

1. The purpose of the article is to teach you how to—
   (A) water ski on one leg
   (B) start on a single ski
   (C) prevent a loss of balance
   (D) conquer the wobble

2. The driver must—
   (A) not keep the same speed
   (B) take a slow curve
   (C) maintain a constant speed
   (D) not create any waves

3. You must remember to—
   (A) take up any slack quickly
   (B) move your body when you wobble
   (C) keep your ski straight up and down
   (D) take the toe of your ski out first

4. To prevent wobbling,—
   (A) lower the knee
   (B) bend your back
   (C) raise the ski higher
   (D) move your ankle

DIRECTIONS: The wake is the rough water directly behind the boat. To cross the wake, just go to one edge of it. If you desire to cross the right side of the wake, first ski to the edge of the left side. Then make a sharp turn to the right so that you will have an almost perpendicular approach. Be sure to keep your knees bent, your back straight, and lean slightly forward at the waist. Your arms should be straight. Your weight should be more to the rear of the ski. The toe will be less likely to dig into the water and cause you to fall.

1. The article shows you how to—
   - (A) approach the wake
   - (B) keep your balance
   - (C) cross the wake
   - (D) jump the wake

2. To cross to the right, you must—
   - (A) approach it slowly
   - (B) first move to the middle
   - (C) first move to the left
   - (D) straighten up

3. It is important to keep your—
   - (A) arms straight
   - (B) back bent
   - (C) knees straight
   - (D) arms bent

4. In order to maintain balance,—
   - (A) keep your weight forward
   - (B) keep your weight backward
   - (C) dig your toes into the water
   - (D) keep weight evenly distributed

DIRECTIONS: Be sure to glide on the left foot. Use your free foot for stopping. To complete the stop, you put your right foot behind your left or gliding foot. Your free foot should be completely sideways to your gliding foot and touching its heel. Your feet form a "T" position. Now slowly lower the free foot until it touches the ice. Make sure the blade is perfectly flat. Put very little pressure on your stopping foot so that you don't stop too suddenly. Just scrape the ice lightly. Keep your arms forward for balance.

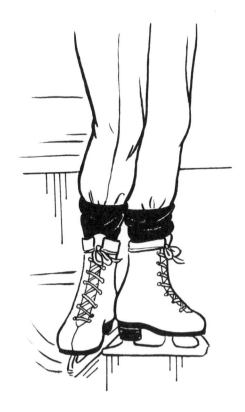

1. The article teaches you how to—
    - (A) glide on ice skates
    - (B) make a "T" stop
    - (C) make a crossover step
    - (D) twirl on ice

2. Your free foot should—
    - (A) strike the ice hard
    - (B) be well out in front
    - (C) exert much pressure
    - (D) touch the ice

3. The blade must be—
    - (A) perfectly flat
    - (B) dull
    - (C) sharp
    - (D) slanted upwards

4. Remember to keep your arms—
    - (A) forward
    - (B) sideways
    - (C) backward
    - (D) down

DIRECTIONS: First prepare the dough. Dissolve one-half package of active dry yeast in mildly warm water. Use three quarters of a cup plus two tablespoons of warm water for the mixture. Measure out three cups of flour, either by the dip-level-pour method or by sifting, and blend in the flour with the yeast and water. After kneading the dough, place it in a greased bowl. Cover the dough and let it rise in a warm place. Divide the dough in half and shape it in two fourteen-inch circles. Now start the sauce and topping. Combine three cups of tomato sauce, seasonings, and Italian cheeses. Spread half the topping, a little oil, and the rest of the topping over each pizza. Bake for thirty minutes. Cut each into slices and serve hot.

1. This article tells you how to—

    (A) make a layer cake   **(B) make pizzas**

    (C) make Italian cheeses   **(D) knead dough**

2. Before measuring out the flour,—

    (A) dissolve yeast in warm water   **(B) knead the dough**

    (C) divide the dough in half   **(D) spread the topping**

3. Before placing the dough in a greased bowl,—

    (A) start the sauce   **(B) divide the dough in half**

    (C) heat the bowl   **(D) knead the dough**

4. Before dividing the dough in half,—

    (A) let it rise   **(B) put it in a cold place**

    (C) start the topping   **(D) bake it for thirty minutes**

DIRECTIONS: Get some vegetable oil. Dip some tissue into it. Then rub the tissue against the white stain on the dark asphalt tile. Rub for approximately one minute. Rub hard and briskly. The heat of friction, or two things rubbing together, helps to dissolve the stain. Repeat the same process a few hours later if necessary. If the stain is an old one, it may take several efforts to remove it. After one or more attempts, that spot in the tile will disappear. The oil should not be used to clean the rest of the tile. It should be used to remove the stain only.

1. This article was written to help you—
   (A) clean the kitchen
   (B) remove scratches
   (C) remove white spots from asphalt tile
   (D) locate food stains

2. After you get some vegetable oil,—
   (A) dip some tissue into it
   (B) boil it
   (C) pour it on the spot
   (D) make a salad

3. Rub hard and briskly because—
   (A) tissue paper is soft
   (B) the heat from friction helps to remove the stain
   (C) vegetable oil is expensive
   (D) the stain may be new

4. After you have rubbed the tile,—
   (A) repeat the process in one minute
   (B) wash the wall
   (C) clean the rest of the asphalt
   (D) do it again in a few hours

DIRECTIONS: Use caution when you work on art projects. Many art supplies are made from toxic materials. These include paint, paint thinner or stripper, model-making glue, and others. Work in an open garage or shed, or use a room in which you can open lots of windows. If you live where windows cannot be opened, set up a small fan to blow the fumes away from you. Then, before you open any of the containers, be sure to read the caution label on each one. This will tell you if the mixture is harmful to breathe or to get in your eyes or on your skin. Then read the instructions about what to do in each of these cases. Wear gloves or a mask if necessary. Keep each container open only while you are using it. Then close it tightly. Store closed containers where children or animals cannot get to them.

1. These directions tell you how to—
   (A) make a model plane
   (B) use toxic art materials safely
   (C) set up a fan
   (D) choose good gloves

2. Work in a room in which you—
   (A) have a large amount of space
   (B) can set up the model to dry
   (C) can keep the windows closed
   (D) have lots of ventilation

3. Before you open any of the containers,—
   (A) read the model kit directions
   (B) put on gloves
   (C) read the caution labels
   (D) choose a paint color

4. Safety materials include—
   (A) pets
   (B) masks
   (C) newspapers
   (D) glue

DIRECTIONS: First remove the tops of two tin cans. Make sure that you leave no sharp edges on the cans. Then punch a small hole in the center of each can's bottom. After that, cut a twenty-foot length of sturdy string. Thread one end of the string through the hole in the bottom of one can. Repeat this procedure with the bottom of the second can. Next tie strong knots in the ends of the string. The knots must prevent the string from slipping out of the hole. Hold one of the tin cans to your ear and hand the other to a friend. Keep a reasonable distance between you and your friend. Now speak to one another. For better sending and receiving over your "telephones," rub the string with wax.

1. These directions teach you how to—
   (A) use the telephone
   (B) discard tin cans
   (C) make strong knots in string
   (D) make tin-can phones

2. Before punching holes in the bottoms of two cans,—
   (A) cut a length of string
   (B) remove the sides
   (C) remove the cans' tops
   (D) hold one can to your ear

3. After threading the string through the hole in the can,—
   (A) tie a knot in the string
   (B) remove the can top
   (C) tie the cans together
   (D) rub the string with glue

4. To improve your "phones,"—
   (A) make the cans bigger
   (B) make the string shorter
   (C) rub the string with wax
   (D) make the holes smaller

DIRECTIONS: To begin with, plan the menus for every meal. This will keep you free of worry during your camping trip. Buy your groceries before you leave home. Make sure that your menus allow you to prepare your meals completely from the groceries you brought from home. To prevent breakage when packing foods, buy foods in plastic containers whenever possible. Cut down the weight of your food by purchasing packaged items instead of canned goods. Use dental floss to tie your dry goods in plastic bags. Be sure to carry with you some of the camping "emergency" foods found in camping catalogs and stores. For convenience, use nonfat dry milk. Margarine is better to use than butter, since it will keep fresh longer.

1. This article tells you how to—
    (A) **plan your camping meals**
    (B) **plan meals for a restaurant**
    (C) **go on a hike**
    (D) **buy packaged goods**

2. Make sure you buy the groceries—
    (A) **in glass jars**
    (B) **at the campsite**
    (C) **in canned goods**
    (D) **before you leave home**

3. Tie your dry goods in plastic bags with—
    (A) **strong rope**
    (B) **guy lines**
    (C) **leather strips**
    (D) **dental floss**

4. A food you should not bring is—
    (A) **butter**
    (B) **"emergency" items**
    (C) **margarine**
    (D) **nonfat dry milk**

DIRECTIONS: First check the tops of your jars, making sure there are no nicks or scratches. Wash and rinse the jars. Leave them in hot water until used. Sort, wash, and rinse your fruit. Place the peaches in a wire basket. Dip the peaches into boiling water for one minute to loosen the skins. After halving the peaches, drop them into salt-vinegar water. Pack the peaches into the jars, cavity-side down. Cover the peaches with hot syrup. Then run a knife along the jar to remove air bubbles. Screw the lid tightly onto the jar. Stand the jars on the rack in the canner; keep the water hot. Put the cover on the canner and boil the jars.

1. This article tells you how to—
   - (A) make a peach dessert
   - (B) pick peaches
   - (C) can peaches
   - (D) buy fresh peaches

2. After sorting and washing the peaches,—
   - (A) wash the jars
   - (B) put them in a wire basket
   - (C) boil them for one hour
   - (D) put the jars in the canner

3. After covering the peaches in the jar with syrup,—
   - (A) pour in a salt-vinegar solution
   - (B) put the jar into boiling water
   - (C) halve the peaches
   - (D) remove air bubbles with a knife

4. After tightening the lids on the jars,—
   - (A) stand the jars on the lids
   - (B) rinse the jars again
   - (C) stand the jars in the canner
   - (D) put the jars in cold water

DIRECTIONS: Make certain all windows and air vents are closed. Start at the top, working down as you go. Dip a sponge or rag into warm soapy water. If the car has recently been waxed or polished, do not use soap or detergents. Simply use warm water and a soft rag. Rub in circular motions. After you have washed a spot, spray that area with the hose. It may be necessary to remove some tar stains with kerosene. Afterward, use a detergent to remove the kerosene. Then wax or polish the places where you used the detergent. Tires should be cleaned with a stiff brush and a detergent. Wash windows inside and out with paper towels. A wet towel should be used first, then a dry one to dry the glass.

1. These instructions tell you how to—
   - **(A) wash your car**
   - **(B) prevent your car from getting dirty**
   - **(C) protect your car from losing its wax shine**
   - **(D) remove stains**

2. If a car has recently been waxed or polished, be sure to—
   - **(A) use soap**
   - **(B) use detergents**
   - **(C) close the vents**
   - **(D) avoid detergents and soap**

3. After you have washed a spot, be sure to—
   - **(A) use a detergent**
   - **(B) spray it with the hose**
   - **(C) use kerosene**
   - **(D) polish it**

4. After you have used kerosene, remove it with—
   - **(A) a detergent**
   - **(B) a stiff brush**
   - **(C) polish**
   - **(D) wax**

DIRECTIONS: If you haven't had any diving experience, it is best to make your first dives from a position as close to the water as possible. In this way you'll get the feel of it and reduce the possibility of danger or mishap.

1. Kneel at the edge of the pool. Hook the toes of one foot over the edge. Make sure that the knee of your other leg is down and on the edge.

2. Put the arms overhead and press against the ears. Take a deep breath. Bend forward with your chin tucked down on your chest, and your head down (in order to keep from "belly flopping").

3. Begin to lean as if to touch the water with your hands. Don't change the position of your arms. Keep them extended and over your ears. Keep leaning and bending forward from the waist until you fall in.

---

1. This article shows you how to make a—
   (A) standing dive
   (B) kneeling dive
   (C) surface dive
   (D) running front dive

2. This kind of dive is for—
   (A) professionals
   (B) adults
   (C) children
   (D) beginners

3. Make certain that—
   (A) both knees are down
   (B) both feet are on the edge
   (C) your head is between your arms
   (D) your head is up

4. It is important to keep—
   (A) the same arm position
   (B) your legs straight
   (C) your eyes closed
   (D) your arms bent

DIRECTIONS: Before tackling the job, be sure you are prepared with a complete set of proper tools. Patch any loose plaster areas on your walls. Then measure the height of your walls from ceiling to baseboard along the floor, including the spots which won't be covered by the wallpaper. Take the measurements to a local dealer and buy the wallpaper of your choice. Apply a layer of paste or, if pre-pasted, wet with a sponge. To hang the paper, unfold the top section and place it on the wall. The top should overlap, or go over, the ceiling joint by about two inches. Fold the rest of the paper onto the wall and smooth it over with a brush. Trim the excess paper from around the door casings and moldings. After removing the excess, use a sponge to rinse the baseboards and casings.

1. These instructions will teach you how to—
   - (A) repair a wall
   - (B) buy the best wallpaper
   - (C) hang wallpaper
   - (D) remove wallpaper

2. After patching any holes in the plaster, you should—
   - (A) hang the wallpaper
   - (B) rinse the baseboards
   - (C) buy the wallpaper
   - (D) measure the walls

3. The top of the wallpaper should—
   - (A) just meet the ceiling joint
   - (B) be put up after the bottom
   - (C) overlap the ceiling joint
   - (D) be trimmed first

4. Rinse the baseboards—
   - (A) before removing the excess
   - (B) before trimming the paper
   - (C) before patching the plaster
   - (D) after removing the excess

DIRECTIONS: First you must decide what kind of bicycle is best for you. Will it be used on a newspaper route? A middleweight bicycle (sixty pounds) with balloon tires is the answer. Do you want a more expensive bicycle for all-around use? This is the recreational bicycle (forty-five pounds), the English racer. A lightweight bicycle (twenty-four pounds) is good for long trips. Unless you buy directly from a bicycle shop, your bicycle will probably arrive not assembled. If so, it will cost a little less, but assembly can be difficult. It is best to deal with a shop. It is best to be measured for the kind of bicycle you want. After you have chosen your bicycle, you will want to select accessories, including a patching kit.

1. This article was written to show you how to—
   (A) price a bicycle　　　**(B) buy a bicycle**
   (C) save money on a bicycle　　**(D) assemble a bicycle**

2. In general, bicycles are divided according to—
   (A) speed　　　**(B) price**
   (C) weight　　　**(D) color**

3. If you do not deal directly with a shop, the bicycle must probably be—
   (A) shipped from England　　**(B) measured**
   (C) described　　　**(D) assembled**

4. Before you choose a patching kit, you should—
   (A) select your bicycle　　**(B) select the type of wheels**
   (C) select the wheel size　　**(D) buy a map**

A. Exercising Your Skill

Directions give you steps to follow. The steps in any directions should be arranged in order. All the information needed to follow the directions should be given. Read the following directions.

HOMEMADE PIZZA

What you need: 1 envelope active dry yeast, 1 cup warm water, $\frac{1}{2}$ teaspoon sugar, 1 teaspoon salt, $3\frac{1}{2}$ cups flour, $\frac{1}{3}$ cup olive oil, 1 can chopped Italian plum tomatoes, pizza pan

What you do:
1. In a bowl, mix yeast and water until yeast is dissolved.
2. Stir in sugar, salt, and flour, and stir until dough is stiff.
3. Knead dough on a floured surface until it is smooth and rubbery.
4. Cover dough with a dishtowel and let stand for one hour.
5. With oiled fingers, press dough into an oiled pizza pan.
6. In a bowl, mix olive oil and tomatoes, and spread evenly on the pizza dough. Add other toppings.
7. Bake in a preheated 425°F oven for half an hour.

Answer these questions about the directions.

- What do you need to know first when you follow a recipe?
- Did these directions put that information first?
- Do these directions tell you in what order to follow the steps?
- Does the order make sense?

B. Expanding Your Skill

Talk with your classmates about how to make pizza. Answer these questions.

- What materials do you need to make pizza?
- What do you do first?
- What else do you do?
- What might happen if you left out Step 3?
- What is the last thing you do?

C. Exploring Language

Giving and following directions step-by-step can be important for numerous things, such as making foods, games, and art projects or taking tests. Work with a group of classmates to think of what materials would be needed for making a model building. To help you think of things, ask yourselves questions like these:

- What size boxes might be used?
- Where would the boxes come from?
- What materials could be used for things like windows, doors, roofs, chimneys, silos, or steps?
- What materials or tools are needed for coloring, cutting, pasting, or stapling?

After the materials are gathered, work with your group to write a set of directions for how to make a particular type of building, such as a restaurant, house, skyscraper, barn, airplane hangar, store, or gas station. Be sure to include clear, easy-to-follow steps in your directions and put them in the right order. Give your group's directions to another group to follow. Then work with your group to follow the directions you receive. When the buildings are finished, make a model community.

D. Expressing Yourself

Choose one of these activities.

1. Find a recipe that tells how to make one of your favorite foods. Bring the recipe to class, and explain how to make the food. You may also bring the things you need to make the food.

2. Choose a set of directions. These can be from a workbook, a game, a kit, or any other place. Read the directions carefully. Then prepare a list of questions about the directions such as: What do you have to do first? Do you need special materials? Exchange directions and questions with a classmate. Answer your classmate's questions.

3. Draw a picture of your pizza. Write a paragraph to tell how it looks, smells, and tastes.

DIRECTIONS: There are several things you can use for a container; a fishbowl, a candy jar, or a big glass are good choices. The most suitable plants for your terrarium are small woodland growths, but any tropical flowers will do. After choosing your plants, plan the arrangement on a piece of paper. Next place coarse stone and charcoal in the bottom of your container. Add two inches of moist soil. Arrange your plants in the soil as you have planned. After the planting, use an atomizer to spray the soil with water. Cover the container with a small piece of glass. Place your completed terrarium where there is good light, but not in direct sunlight. This "plant world under glass" will spring to life before you know it.

1. These instructions will help you—
   - **(A) tend a garden**
   - **(C) find tropical flowers**
   - **(B) make paper flowers**
   - **(D) build a terrarium**

2. Before filling the terrarium, you should—
   - **(A) use an atomizer**
   - **(C) place it in good light**
   - **(B) plan the plant arrangement**
   - **(D) cover the container**

3. The moist soil should be added after—
   - **(A) you use the atomizer**
   - **(C) the stone and charcoal**
   - **(B) the cover is removed**
   - **(D) the terrarium is covered**

4. After spraying the soil, you should—
   - **(A) add more dirt**
   - **(C) arrange the plants**
   - **(B) add the charcoal**
   - **(D) cover the container**

DIRECTIONS: Relax and don't throw yourself into a panic. Concentrate on how you traveled. Mark a tree on all sides so that you can spot it from any direction. Then walk in a circle around the tree examining the surrounding area. Be sure to leave a note for your fellow hikers, telling them the direction in which you headed. Try to locate a stream. Follow it downstream; it will probably lead you to a town or village. Always look for high ground. Look and call out from a hill or tall tree. Follow telephone wires, power lines, and the sounds of cars; these will lead you to civilization. If possible, send up a smoke signal. Should darkness fall while you are still lost, stay where you are and look for shelter.

1. These directions show you how to—
   - (A) start a camping trip
   - (B) start a fire
   - (C) climb a tree
   - (D) react if you become lost

2. Before examining the surrounding ground,—
   - (A) find a stream
   - (B) mark a tree
   - (C) start a fire
   - (D) find shelter

3. Should you find a stream, follow it—
   - (A) upstream
   - (B) toward telephone lines
   - (C) downstream
   - (D) even after dark

4. If darkness falls and you're still lost,—
   - (A) follow the sound of autos
   - (B) locate a stream
   - (C) mark a tree
   - (D) stay where you are

DIRECTIONS: Before cooking, wipe the roast with a wet cloth, followed by a dry one. Season the meat now or halfway through roasting. If seasoning with garlic, make tiny cuts in the meat and insert the garlic with the knife point. Then put the roast on the rack in the roasting pan with the fat side up. Cover veal and lamb with strips of bacon. Place the meat thermometer in the roast at this time or when the meat is slightly cooked. Make sure that the thermometer is in the center of the thickest part of the roast, not touching bone, fat, or gristle. With a thin roast, insert the thermometer on a slant.

1. These instructions tell you how to—
   - (A) carve meats
   - (B) remove the fat from roasts
   - (C) build a meat thermometer
   - (D) prepare roasts for the oven

2. Before seasoning the meat,—
   - (A) wipe the roast with a wet cloth
   - (B) cover it with bacon
   - (C) put in the thermometer
   - (D) completely cook it

3. Put the roast in the roasting pan—
   - (A) fat side down
   - (B) with the thermometer in the fat
   - (C) fat side up
   - (D) on a slant

4. With a thin roast, place the thermometer—
   - (A) on a slant
   - (B) in the fat
   - (C) in the thickest section
   - (D) so that it rests on a bone

UNIT 42

DIRECTIONS: Is your garage or attic an accident waiting to happen? Never pile kerosene-soaked cleaning rags in an airless space because they can catch fire. Throw them out. A fire could then ignite piles of newspapers, so take newspapers to a recycling center on a regular basis. People can slip in puddles of water or shock themselves while using an electrical tool. Clean up puddles. Don't risk injurious falls by climbing on ladders or stacked up material. Secure garbage in a tight container until pickup day, or it may attract flies and rats.

1. These directions tell you how to—
  (A) help someone who has fallen
  (B) become a safety expert
  (C) pile papers in a garage
  (D) keep a garage or basement safe

2. If you have cleaning rags piled in a corner,—
  (A) put them in water
  (B) throw them out
  (C) put them on a ladder
  (D) use them to start fires

3. When using an electrical tool,—
  (A) always stand on a ladder
  (B) stay near an open window
  (C) never stand in water
  (D) always have the radio on

4. Garbage stored in insecure containers—
  (A) can cause falls
  (B) can lead to fires
  (C) can cause shocks
  (D) can attract rats and flies

DIRECTIONS: First lay two bricks on a flat surface. Place a metal rod across the bricks (a metal coathanger will do). Then place a third brick on one end of the rod to prevent it from moving. Place a darning needle under the other end of the rod. Next make a pointer from a sheet of cardboard or a drinking straw and glue it to the end of the darning needle. Construct a scale in the form of a half-circle on a card and place it behind the needle. Then hold a burning candle (use caution at this point) under the metal rod, moving it slowly back and forth along its length. Watch the pointer as the rod heats up. It will move, showing that the rod has expanded with the heat.

1. This article tells you how to—
   (A) identify types of metal
   (B) build a heater
   (C) prove metal expands when heated
   (D) forge a metal rod

2. The third brick should be placed—
   (A) next to the other bricks
   (B) on one end of the rod
   (C) on top of the darning needle
   (D) behind the needle

3. The pointer should be glued to—
   (A) the third brick
   (B) the scale
   (C) the metal rod
   (D) the darning needle

4. As the pointer moves, it shows that—
   (A) the bricks are heating up
   (B) metal shrinks when heated
   (C) metal expands upon heating
   (D) the rod is rolling

DIRECTIONS: Stand well back of the end line in the service area. Keep your left foot in front of your right. Your knees should be slightly flexed and your body bent forward. Hold the volleyball with your left hand. Keep your left arm straight and in a direct line with your right arm. As you bring your right arm back and swing it forward, make sure the elbow is kept straight. Just before contact, gently toss the ball a few inches into the air. Strike the lower part of the ball with either your knuckles or the heel of your open hand. Keep your wrist stiff. Just as you make your swing, step with your left foot and shift your weight to it. Make sure that you don't step so far forward that you touch the end line so that your serve does not count.

1. The selection tells you how to—
   - (A) serve a volleyball
   - (B) shoot a volleyball
   - (C) contact a volleyball
   - (D) pass a volleyball

2. Hold the volleyball with—
   - (A) your left hand
   - (B) your right hand
   - (C) both hands
   - (D) neither hand

3. You are supposed to hit the ball—
   - (A) on the side
   - (B) on the top
   - (C) on the lower side
   - (D) in the middle

4. You should stand well back so you won't—
   - (A) hit too far
   - (B) contact your own player
   - (C) break a rule
   - (D) get enough power

DIRECTIONS: Find an empty flour sack or sugar bag, about six feet of very strong rope, two fourteen-inch lengths of strong string, and enough old papers with which to stuff the bag. Then wad sheets of paper into hard balls and press them into the sack until you have a pile two feet high. Gather the sack together and tie some string tightly around it. Make a double knot to be sure the paper will remain in the sack. Then attach another string to the knot at the sack's top. The punching bag is now ready to be suspended at the proper height from a beam or the top of a door frame. Use a big screw eye to hang the bag from a piece of wood.

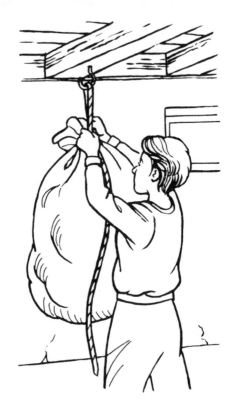

1. This article tells you how to—
   (A) make a punching bag
   (B) hang a wall decoration
   (C) make a garbage sack
   (D) make a bag puppet

2. Fill the sack with—
   (A) one foot of paper
   (B) wadded paper
   (C) rocks
   (D) six feet of rope

3. Before attaching the bag to a beam,—
   (A) fill it with flour
   (B) make a double knot in the bag's string
   (C) close the bag with a screw eye
   (D) begin to punch it

4. To hang the bag from the wood, use—
   (A) light string
   (B) a large screw eye
   (C) old newspapers
   (D) a sticky glue

DIRECTIONS: First heat your oven to 450°. Next set out an ungreased baking sheet. Then stir together a mixture of two cups of all-purpose flour, two teaspoons of baking powder, and a half teaspoon of salt. Add to that a quarter of a cup of shortening and three quarters of a cup of milk. Stir this together with a fork until the mixture can be formed into balls. Turn the dough onto a lightly floured board and knead by folding and pressing. Then, with a rolling pin, roll the dough to one-half-inch thickness. Cut the biscuits with a round cutter, and use a spatula to place them on the baking sheet. To make crusty biscuits, place the cut pieces of dough about an inch apart. Bake for about twelve minutes or until brown.

1. These directions show you how to—
   - **(A) make rolled biscuits**
   - **(B) bake a cake**
   - **(C) make a pizza crust**
   - **(D) make corn muffins**

2. To the flour, baking powder, salt, and shortening, add—
   - **(A) three quarters of a cup of sugar**
   - **(B) three quarters of a cup of baking soda**
   - **(C) three cups of milk**
   - **(D) three quarters of a cup of milk**

3. After kneading the dough,—
   - **(A) heat the oven**
   - **(B) form it into balls**
   - **(C) add the milk**
   - **(D) roll it to one-half-inch thickness**

4. To make the biscuits crusty,—
   - **(A) flatten out the dough with a spatula**
   - **(B) keep the dough pieces an inch apart**
   - **(C) don't knead the dough**
   - **(D) use more milk**

DIRECTIONS: You can make different musical sounds with a straw. Cut a triangular shape at one end of it. Place that end in your mouth and blow, pursing your lips while doing so. A nice deep sound comes out. If you make the straw shorter, the sound that comes out will be higher. This is because the air in a shorter straw vibrates, or moves, faster than the air in a longer straw. The faster the air vibrates, the higher the pitch.

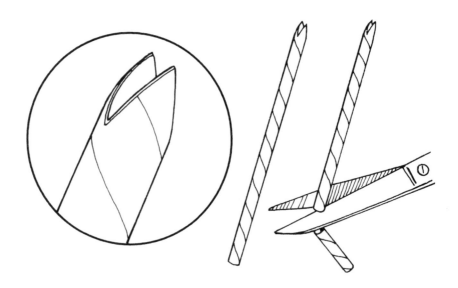

1. These directions tell you how to get different sounds from a—
   - (A) horn
   - (B) soda
   - (C) straw
   - (D) weed

2. The shape you cut at one end is like a—
   - (A) rectangle
   - (B) triangle
   - (C) consonant
   - (D) box

3. When you blow into that end, be sure to—
   - (A) drop your jaw
   - (B) purse your lips
   - (C) grit your teeth
   - (D) bite it

4. If you shorten the length of the straw, the pitch becomes—
   - (A) slower
   - (B) deeper
   - (C) higher
   - (D) louder

DIRECTIONS: Fingernail polish can come in handy if a tick has attached itself to your skin. Brush the polish over the head of the tick and around the adjoining area. This will cut off the tick's air supply. As soon as the tick is unable to get air, it will detach itself from your skin in a matter of seconds. If you don't have nail polish handy, or if the tick is already dead, use tweezers to remove it. First, dab the area with an antiseptic that will kill germs. Then, grasp the tick firmly with the tweezers, as near to the point of attachment as possible. Pull slowly and steadily. Do not jerk, or part of the tick may remain buried in your skin. After the tick has been removed, apply an antiseptic to the wound.

1. These directions give you two ways to—
   (A) use tweezers
   (B) kill a tick
   (C) remove a tick
   (D) use fingernail polish

2. The easiest method is to—
   (A) cover it with fingernail polish
   (B) freeze it
   (C) jerk it with tweezers
   (D) cover it with antiseptic

3. If the tick can't get air, it will—
   (A) breathe deeper
   (B) detach itself
   (C) burrow into the skin
   (D) bite the victim

4. After removing the insect, cover the wound with—
   (A) an antiseptic
   (B) a bandage
   (C) fingernail polish
   (D) clean water

DIRECTIONS: To remove orange juice stains from a white enamel refrigerator door, try bleaching out the stains with a mild solution of household bleach and water. If this doesn't work, scrub the stains with kerosene and a plastic dish scrubber. To get rid of the strong smell of the kerosene, wipe the treated area with vinegar. Half a lemon dipped into borax, another kind of cleaning agent, can also be rubbed over the stains to get rid of them.

1. This article gives three possible methods for—

    (A) burning kerosene   **(B) removing stains**

    (C) storing orange juice   **(D) cooking with vinegar**

2. Removal of stains could occur with a treatment of—

    (A) vinegar and orange juice   **(B) water and vinegar**

    (C) bleach and water   **(D) water and orange juice**

3. A plastic dish scrubber can be used to rub stains with—

    (A) kerosene   **(B) cleanser**

    (C) paint   **(D) water**

4. Stains can also be rubbed with half a lemon dipped into—

    (A) coffee   **(B) water**

    (C) jam   **(D) borax**

DIRECTIONS: To make bookmarks that are practical and not likely to get lost, use the corners of envelopes. Cut the bottom right-hand corner of a used envelope as shown in the picture. Decorate the front by drawing a picture or design with paints, crayons, or felt-tipped pens. Such a bookmark can be made quickly. It can be slipped easily and securely over the corner of a page to mark a place. Bookmarks make useful and attractive presents. Enclose them in the birthday and holiday cards you send to your friends.

1. These instructions are for making bookmarks with—
   (A) cardboard
   (B) toothpicks
   (C) envelopes
   (D) cloth

2. The part of an envelope to use is the—
   (A) right-hand bottom corner
   (B) sticky flap on back
   (C) postmarked area
   (D) left-hand top corner

3. The bookmark can be decorated by using—
   (A) wood-burning tools
   (B) felt-tipped pens
   (C) toothpaste tubes
   (D) hairspray cans

4. This type of bookmark goes—
   (A) between the book's covers
   (B) over the corner of a page
   (C) on the title page
   (D) into a pocket

The Last L A P
Language Activity Pages

A. Exercising Your Skill

Sometimes illustrations can make the directions clearer. Read these directions.

PAPER HELICOPTER

What you need: a sheet of $8\frac{1}{2}$ x 11-inch paper, scissors, paper clips

What to do:

1. Fold the paper in half.
2. At the top and halfway down each side of the paper, cut out three small triangles.
3. On the top half, cut a slit in the middle down as far as the fold.
4. Cut in a little further from the side triangles, and fold the bottom sides to the middle. Hold the sides together with one or two small paper clips.
5. Fold one of the flaps forward and one backward.
6. Decorate your helicopter with drawings or stickers.
7. Write a name for the helicopter on its side.
8. Toss the helicopter in the air, and watch it spin down!

Which steps would be clearer with illustrations? Draw pictures to make the directions clearer.

B. Expanding Your Skill

Read the following list of topics. Discuss the topics with your classmates. Decide which topics could best be explained if illustrations were included with the written steps.

How to Use a Computer
How to Square-Dance
How to Paddle a Canoe
How to Fold a Paper Bird
How to Make a Kite
How to Play Checkers
How to Mark an Answer
How to Play Hockey

C. Exploring Language

The directions below are not well written. They contain information that is not needed. They do not list the materials that are needed. The steps are not in order, and there are no signal words to help make the order clear. Improve and rewrite the directions. Add illustrations to make the directions clearer.

Candles add a beautiful light to a room, and they're easy to make. You can color the candle wax by melting a crayon in it. If you have a box of 64 crayons, that gives you a lot of colors to choose from! You have to melt the candle wax in a double boiler, or you can do it in a clean tin can placed in a saucepan of hot water. Tie one end of a piece of cotton string or regular candle wick to a thumbtack. Tie the other end to a stick or pencil. Lay the pencil across the top of the mold you are using so that the thumbtack is suspended in the mold. For a mold, you can use an empty milk carton. If you don't like square candles, you could use a cardboard frozen juice can instead. Don't melt the wax until your wick is in place. Pour the melted wax into the mold. After the melted wax has cooled and hardened, just peel off the mold.

D. Expressing Yourself

Choose one of these activities.

1. Write a paragraph telling how to do one of the following things. Remember to list the materials that are needed, if any. Use time-order words to show the order of the steps. Add illustrations if they will help.
   1. fly a kite
   2. get emergency help
   3. study for a test
   4. play the drums
   5. make a shell necklace
   6. make applesauce

2. Prepare illustrated directions for everyday situations, such as addressing an envelope, going through a subway turnstile, or getting something to eat in the school cafeteria.